Written by
LIAM O'DONNELL

Illustrated by
MIKE ROOTH

This story is set in Britain more than 2,000 years ago. Each chapter ends with a non-fiction page that gives more information about real people's lives and actual events at that time.

OXFORD
UNIVERSITY PRESS

CHARACTERS

NIALL AND ROSS

JULIUS CAESAR

CHIEFTAIN

NIALL'S FATHER

ROSS'S FATHER

GOBAN

NESSA

REAL PERSON IN HISTORY

JULIUS CAESAR (100–44 BC/BCE): The ruler of the Roman Empire and one of history's greatest generals. He defeated many Celtic tribes.

FICTIONAL CHARACTERS

ROSS: The 13-year-old son of a Celtic farmer who hopes to become a fierce warrior.

NIALL: Ross's best friend and the son of a Celtic noble.

CHIEFTAIN: The village chief who defends his lands against the Romans.

NIALL'S FATHER: A Celtic noble who fights alongside his chieftain.

ROSS'S FATHER: He thinks Ross is too young to go into battle.

GOBAN: A Celtic warrior who is always picking on Ross and Niall.

NESSA: Niall's sister who is an artist.

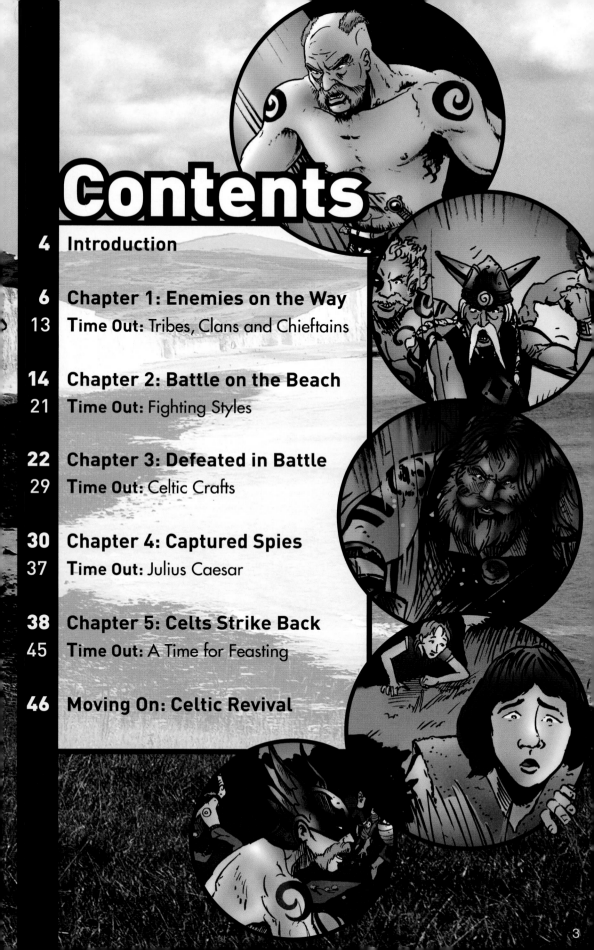

Contents

When we speak of the Celts today, we think of the people of Scotland, Wales and Ireland. But 2,500 years ago, the Celts were made up of different groups called tribes, and they were spread across Europe. They settled in many different regions, from Britain to Bulgaria, from Germany to Egypt. They spoke related languages and followed the same ways of life. However, they had no single leader and were not united as one nation.

Celtic warriors

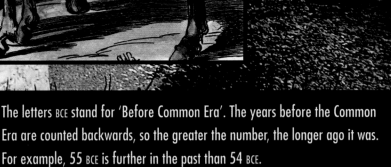

TIMELINE

The letters BCE stand for 'Before Common Era'. The years before the Common Era are counted backwards, so the greater the number, the longer ago it was. For example, 55 BCE is further in the past than 54 BCE.

55 BC/BCE »	54 BC/BCE »	AD/CE 43 »	AD/CE 60 »
Julius Caesar makes his first attempt to conquer Britain, but fails.	Caesar conquers the south of Britain, but returns to Europe.	The Romans return and occupy the southeast of Britain. Britain becomes a Roman province.	Boudicca, a Celtic queen, leads a revolt against the Romans. She is defeated the next year.

The Romans were a powerful force across Europe. By the first century BC/BCE, the Romans had conquered most of the Celtic tribes on the European continent. Only the Celts who lived on the islands of Britain still kept their way of life.

In 55 BC/BCE, a powerful Roman general named Julius Caesar planned to change all that …

Statue of Julius Caesar

This story is set in an actual time in history, although some of the events are fictional. Real events during this period are shown on the timeline below.

122 »	410 »	450 »	1536 »	1707 »
The Romans build Hadrian's Wall to keep Celtic tribes in Scotland from attacking Roman settlements.	The Roman army withdraws from Britain.	Anglo-Saxon tribes from Europe invade Britain and settle. Celts are driven to the west and north of the island.	Wales is united with England.	Scotland is united with England.

11

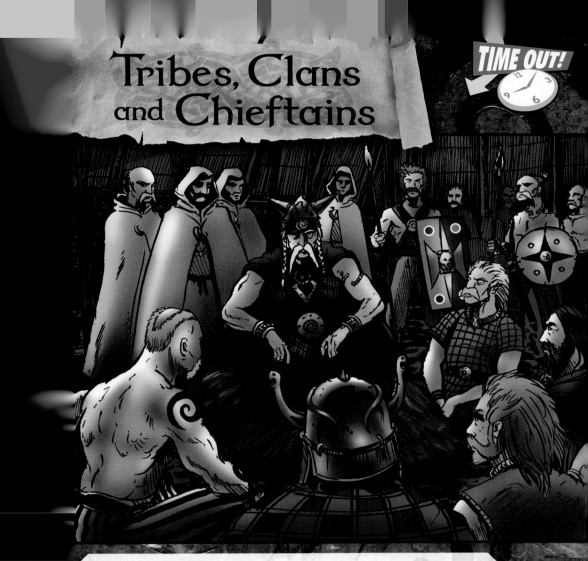

Tribes, Clans and Chieftains

TIME OUT!

The Celts lived in groups called tribes. Each tribe had several clans or family groups.

Celtic tribes often fought one another for land or other resources. However, when threatened by an outside force, like the Romans, the tribes would come together and fight side by side.

A chieftain ruled over each tribe and protected it from enemies. He had the help of nobles, priests and warriors. The nobles were the richest people of each clan. They were landowners. The priests led religious ceremonies to honour Celtic gods and goddesses. The warriors led the tribe into battle.

Fighting Styles

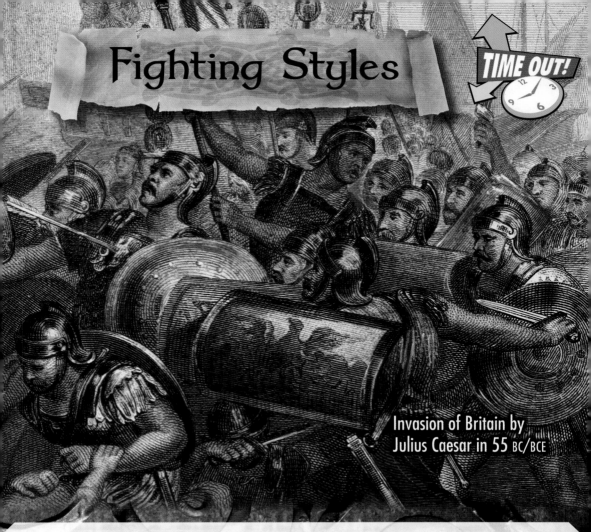

Invasion of Britain by Julius Caesar in 55 BC/BCE

Celt warriors fought in a wild and furious way. To frighten their enemies, they painted themselves blue with a plant called woad and spiked their hair. They charged into battle making a lot of noise – yelling, screeching their bagpipes and bellowing their horns.

The Celts fought with iron swords, spears, slingshots and bows and arrows. Some of them wore helmets and carried wooden shields for protection. Others rushed into battle wearing nothing at all, except for necklaces of twisted metal called torcs.

Roman troops were organised and well trained. They fought as a team. Across Europe, the smaller, well-trained Roman armies easily defeated the much larger but wilder armies of the Celts.

THE DEFEATED CELTS DISCUSS THE INVADING ROMAN ARMY AND ITS POWERFUL LEADER, JULIUS CAESAR.

THE LEADERS AND THE NOBLES OF THE NEARBY TRIBES HAVE COME TOGETHER. WE'LL DRIVE THE ROMAN ARMY FROM OUR LANDS YET!

SHSSH ... BE QUIET, NIALL! AND BE CAREFUL. YOU DON'T WANT TO FALL THROUGH AND LAND ON YOUR FATHER'S SPEAR!

WE CANNOT DEFEAT JULIUS CAESAR. HIS ARMIES HAVE MARCHED ACROSS THE LAND AND TAKEN OVER EVERYTHING.

I AGREE. LET'S MEET WITH CAESAR AND SURRENDER.

Celtic Crafts

The Celts were talented artists and craftsmen. They were especially famous for their metalwork and cloth weaving.

Torc

Metalwork: The Celts mined iron, copper and tin to make beautiful jewellery and other items.

Brooch

Shield

Tartan: The descendants of the Celts in Scotland are still famous for their tartan cloth. Each clan or family group has its own special tartan design.

Tartan cloth was admired by the Greek historian Diodorus Siculus (about 30 BC/BCE). He wrote:

The Celts wear brightly coloured and embroidered shirts with trousers and cloaks … these cloaks are striped or chequered in design, with the separate checks close together and in various colours.

Chapter 4: CAPTURED SPIES

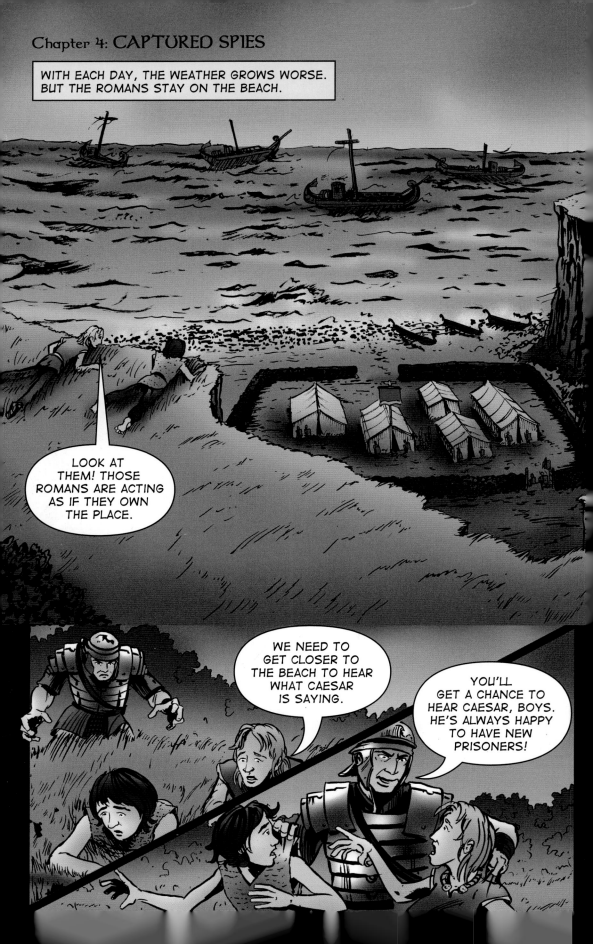

Julius Caesar

TIME OUT!

Julius Caesar (100–44 BC/BCE) was a brilliant Roman general. He conquered much of central Europe, including Gaul (present-day France) which had been Celtic territory. Julius Caesar was so successful in war that his words *Veni, vidi, vici* (Latin for 'I came, I saw, I conquered') have become famous all over the world.

One place that Caesar could not easily conquer was Britain. In 55 BC/BCE, he tried to invade, but bad weather caused him to leave after three months. He tried again the next year, but was again defeated by the bad British weather.

Caesar was a harsh dictator who made many enemies among his own people. In 44 BC/BCE, he was killed by his fellow Romans.

Murder of Julius Caesar

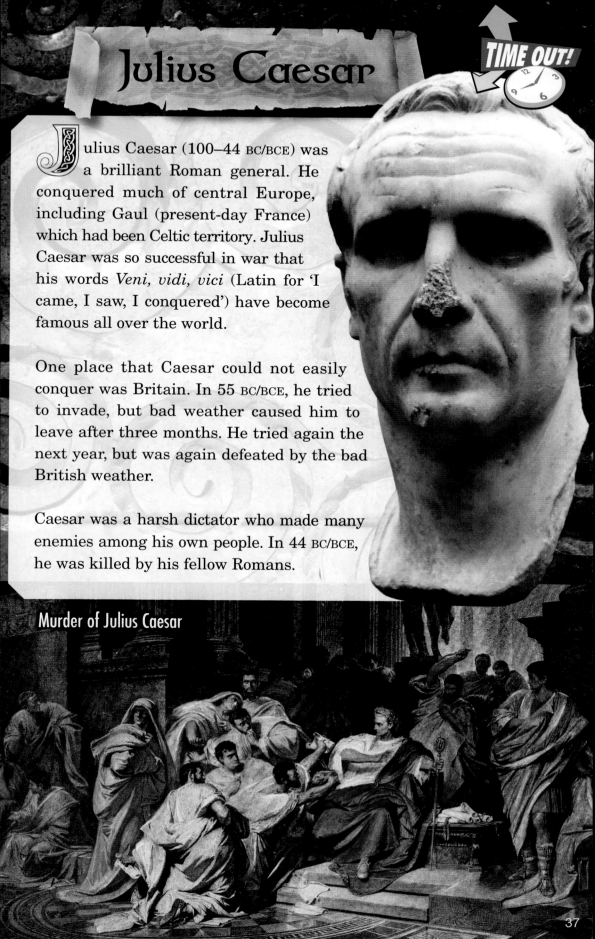

44

A Time for Feasting

Celts loved feasting. At feasts, food and drink were served all day and all night. Celtic feasts were rowdy and noisy, and often ended with the guests fighting one another!

Women cooked and served the food, but only men were allowed to attend feasts. The nobles and warriors sat around in a circle on thick furs. They ate food and listened to musicians sing songs of praise about the chieftain and battle heroes.

The champion's portion was the choice of the finest meat. It was served to the guest of honour, the bravest hero. If another warrior thought he deserved the champion's portion, he could challenge the guest of honour. The two men would then fight over the meat, providing more entertainment for the other guests!

CELTIC

It was not until AD/CE 43, almost 100 years later, that Rome finally conquered Britain and turned it into a Roman colony.

The Romans stayed in Britain for 400 years. The Celts, especially in the southeast of the island, took on Roman ways. Then the Roman Empire was attacked by barbarians. In 410, the Roman army left the shores of Britain. The next people to invade were the Angles and the Saxons, ancestors of the English.

The Celts, once widespread across Europe, were pushed to the northern and western edges of Britain – to Wales, Scotland and Ireland. Today, young people in these countries are rediscovering the beauty of Celtic languages, music and art. The ancient culture of the Celts lives on in the modern world.

REVIVAL

A re-enactment of a battle scene

Tin whistle

Irish dancing

INDEX

GLOSSARY

chariot – a horse-drawn vehicle with two wheels used in ancient times

chieftain – the leader of a tribe

conquered – defeated

reward – something given to you because you have done something good

savages – people thought to be uncivilised

slave – a person who is owned by another person and works without being paid

surrender – to stop fighting and give yourself up to the enemy

tribe – a group of families living in one area as a group, ruled by a chieftain

warrior – a person who fights in a battle